The Buzzing Bee

by Holly Harper
illustrated by Liza Lewis

OXFORD
UNIVERSITY PRESS

Dad and Ella sit on the rug.

Ella gets her jam bun.

I can see a buzzing bee!

Get off the jam, bee!

Dad gets in the rocket.

I see the buzzing bee.
Keep off!

Get off, bee!

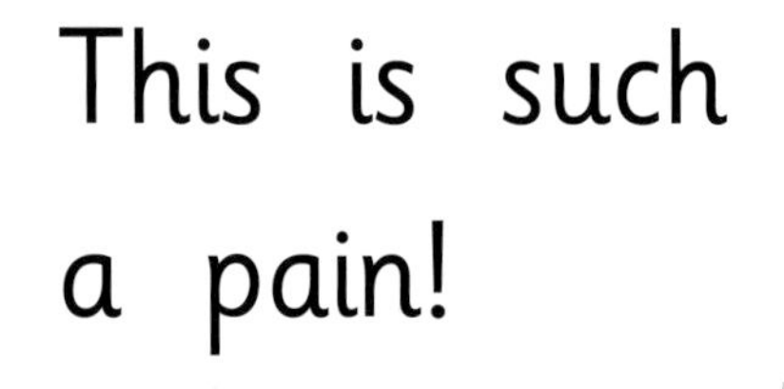
This is such
a pain!

Dad is up high.

I can see the
buzzing bee.

Dad is in a boat.
He can not wait to go.

Dad will put up a fight.

Dad is soaking wet.

That bee
is a pain!

Wait! We need
to sit.

Dad gets jam.
Ella gets jam.
The buzzing bee gets jam!